JOSEPH
the coat of many colors

Written and illustrated by
GEOFFREY BUTCHER

Rourke Publications, Inc.
A Little Shepherd Book
Vero Beach, FL 32964

Joseph's father loved him more than his older brothers.

He gave Joseph a coat made of many colors.

Joseph had dreams. He said that he would rule over his brothers. His dreams told that to him.

The brothers were mad. They wanted to get rid of him.

Joseph's father put some food in a sack. He told Joseph to take the sack to his brothers.

He came to the place where
they were watching the sheep.
They threw him down a well.

The brothers argued about what to do next. A caravan of merchants came.

His brothers decided to sell Joseph to the merchants as a slave.

The brothers dipped Joseph's coat in the blood of a dead goat.

They told their father that Joseph had been killed by a wild animal.

Meanwhile Joseph had been taken to Egypt by the merchants.

There they sold him to Potiphar, a captain of Pharaoh's guard.

Potiphar could tell that Joseph was very smart. He put Joseph in charge of his house.

Potiphar's wife was jealous.
She had Joseph put into
prison.

In prison Joseph told two other prisoners what their dreams meant.

When Pharoah heard of this he sent for Joseph. He wanted to discover the meaning of his own dreams.

Joseph told Pharaoh that there would be seven years of plenty and seven years of hunger.

Pharoah put Joseph in charge
of storing food. They would
need food during the bad years.

When the bad years came there was food in the storehouses of Egypt.

Joseph became the most important man in Egypt after Pharoah himself.

At home Joseph's father and brothers were hungry. They had no food stored.

The father sent his sons to Egypt to try to buy food.

In Egypt Joseph sold them corn. The brothers did not know who he was.

When no one was looking, Joseph had a silver cup put into their sack.

The brothers were arrested for stealing the silver cup.

They were very much afraid. At last they knew who Joseph was.

Joseph forgave them. He said that God had sent him to Egypt. He would save them all from famine.

Questions to help you understand

1. What did Joseph's father give him?
2. Why were Joseph's brothers jealous of him?
3. What did Joseph tell Pharoah about his dreams?
4. How did Joseph meet his brothers again?